# Read It, Don't Eat It!

## Ian Schoenherr

SCHOLASTIC INC.

New York  Toronto  London  Auckland
Sydney  Mexico City  New Delhi  Hong Kong

To the bibliothecarians, bibliopolists, and bibliophiles
who have fed me,
with hopes that they can digest this.
And especial thanks to Linda Lapides for the spark,
and to Kathy, Marcia, Virginia, and Paul for the spur.

ISBN 978-0-545-29652-6

12 11 10 9 8 7 6 5 4 3 2          11 12 13 14 15/0

Printed in the U.S.A.          40

First Scholastic printing, September 2010

Permanent ink and acrylic paint on watercolor paper
were used to prepare the full-color art.
The text type is hand lettered.

Read it,
don't eat it.

No dog-ears, please.

Find someplace else to sneeze.

# Borrow, don't steal.

TRY *not to squeal.*

Rips and tears won't magically heal.

# Don't overdue it, just renew it.

(Really, now, there's nothing to it.)

Leave no trace
(or at least erase).

Don't censor, delete, or deface.

It's not a platter,
or a stool.

Be careful with it at the pool.

Don't leave it in the rain or sun.

Please return it when you're done.

Share with a friend,
a sister, a brother.

# Now go out and get another.